Amazing Paper Tricks that really work

Paul Jackson

CONTENTS

Introduction 2
Read This! 2
Symbols 3
Magic Flute 4
Impossible Illusion 6
Square or Cross? 8
Helicopter 10
Good Day, Bad Day? 12
Shapeshifter 14
Banger! 17
Downside Up 20
S-t-r-e-t-c-h 23
Exploding Underpants 26
Hide and Seek 29

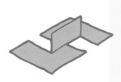

a Mary Ford Book

Introduction

Think how many times a day you use or touch things made from paper. Paper is very familiar to us and we all think we know it well. But we don't!!

Paper has a wonderful secret. Just by adding a few simple folds or cuts it can be used to make amazing tricks and curiosities. This book shows you the best of them, old and new, collected from around the world. Some are funny, others strange or beautiful, but they are all very, very clever and easy to make.

The best way to enjoy this book is to learn a few favourites, then to share them with friends. But before you begin, please read 'Read This!' below, and look at the 'Symbols' page opposite. Together, they will give you all you need to know to get you started in the weird, whacky world of *Amazing Paper Tricks*.

Read This!

Here are some important tips to help you make your tricks work well.

● *Find a Good Place to Work*. Fold the paper on a hard, flat surface so that you can make firm creases. If you are using scissors and glue, don't work on someone's best table without permission, and remember to put newspaper on it first.

● *Ask an Adult*. If you aren't very good with scissors, ask an adult to help you.

● *Follow the Steps Carefully*. When making a trick, keep checking to make sure that it looks exactly like the step-by-step drawings. If it doesn't … don't panic! Just go back one or two steps until what you are making looks like an earlier drawing, then try again. Also, don't just look at the drawings – read the instructions too!

● *Work Slowly*. Don't rush! All the paper tricks in the book will work better and look better if you make them slowly and carefully. Sometimes, you may need to make a trick two or three times before you can make it really well.

● *Good Paper*. Try out the tricks using clean, uncrumpled paper. Note paper and printer paper are best. Use A4 or $8^1/_2$ x 11in size or bigger where suggested. When you're ready, use bright coloured paper to make your paper tricks really amazing!

Symbols

These simple symbols explain how to make the tricks in the book. If you see a symbol in the instructions and you don't understand it, look back to this page to see what it means.

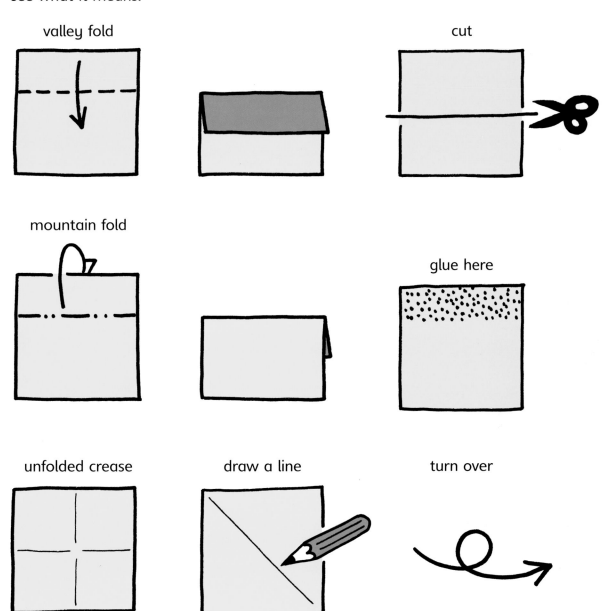

valley fold

cut

mountain fold

glue here

unfolded crease

draw a line

turn over

Magic Flute

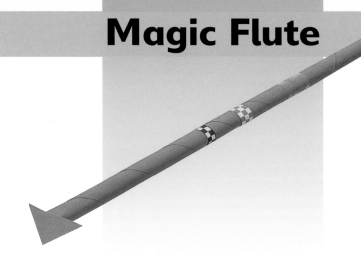

There are a few brilliant paper noise makers and this is probably the very best. It is 'magic' because you can play it, but your friends cannot – the secret is to *breathe in, not blow!*

❶

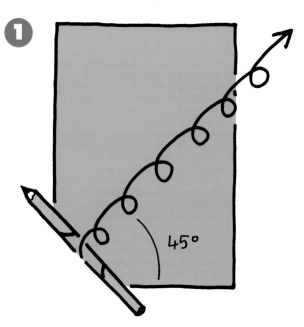

45°

Neatly roll up a pencil or pen inside a tube of paper, rolling across at 45° from the corner.

❷

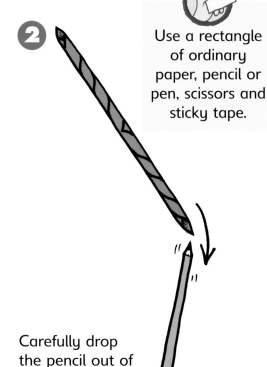

Carefully drop the pencil out of the tube.

3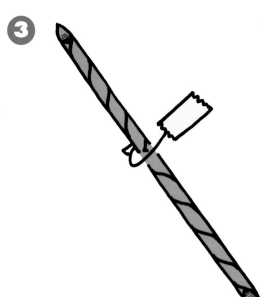

Hold the tube together with a small piece of sticky tape wrapped around the middle.

4

With scissors, very carefully cut almost all the way across the tube, beginning the cut *exactly* at the bottom end of the opening.

5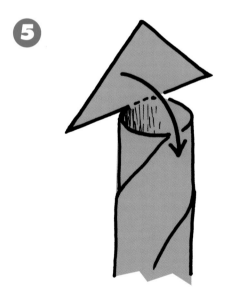

The cut will create a flat triangle. Fold it over the flat end of the tube. It should completely cover the opening.

6

To make it play, put the uncut end into your mouth and gently breathe in. Don't blow!

Impossible Illusion

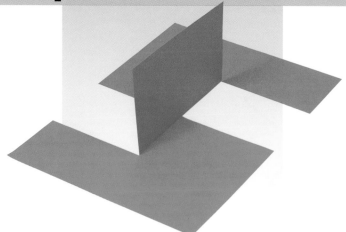

This classic illusion is totally baffling when you see it for the first time, but amazingly simple to make. Show it to your friends, then challenge them to copy it, but without touching it. They will do well to work it out!

Use a rectangle of plain paper, any size, pencil, ruler and scissors.

1

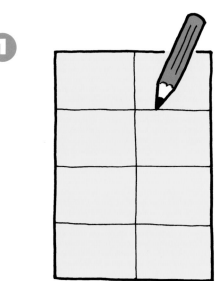

With a pencil and ruler, draw a long centre line down the middle, then a short centre line across the middle, then quarter lines across the middle.

2

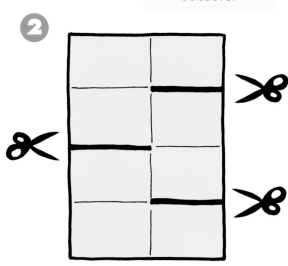

Make three cuts to the centre line, as shown. Rub out the unwanted pencil lines.

3

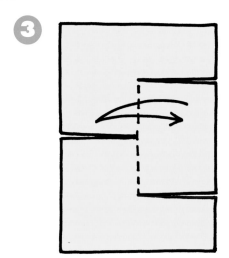

Crease and fold down the middle.

4

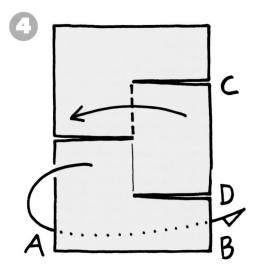

Now, twist over the bottom edge of the sheet, so that A and B swap places, and edges CD moves across to the left. Look at the drawing to see the result.

5

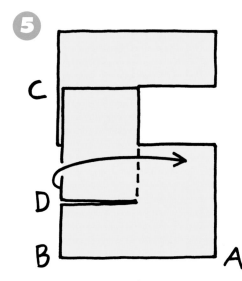

Finally, make a short crease where shown to lift edge CD, so that it stands upright.

6

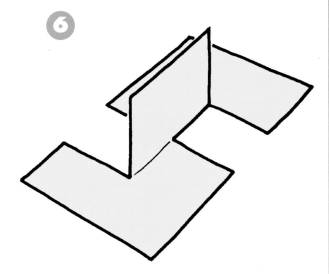

Complete.

Square or Cross?

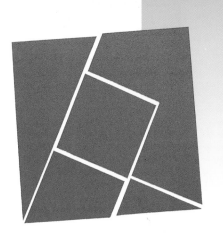

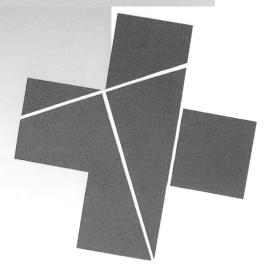

Here's a clever and rather beautiful trick by the famous 19th century American puzzlist, Sam Loyd. It mysteriously changes a square into other shapes.

Use a square of paper 10 x 10cm (4 x 4in), ruler, pencil and scissors.

1

$\frac{1}{2}$

$\frac{1}{2}$

$\frac{1}{2}$

$\frac{1}{2}$

With a ruler and pencil, measure and mark the exact centre point of each edge.

2

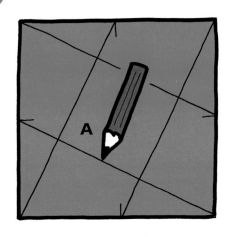

A

Then draw four lines as shown, connecting the centre points with an opposite corner.

3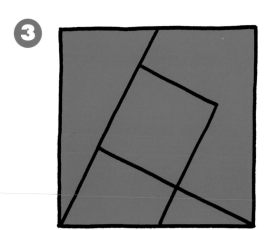

Rub out some of the lines so that these ones remain. Then, carefully cut along the lines to make five separate pieces.

4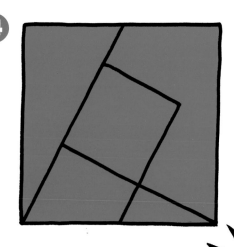

The five pieces in the square can be re-arranged to make other shapes, including ...

5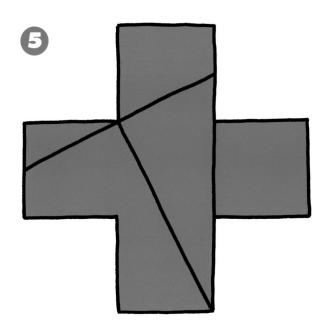

... a cross! Can you re-arrange them again to make a triangle, a rectangle and other simple shapes?

Helicopter

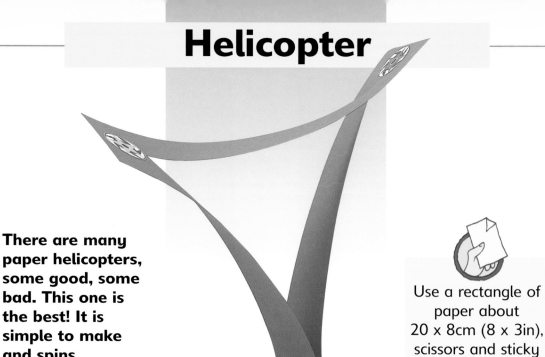

There are many paper helicopters, some good, some bad. This one is the best! It is simple to make and spins superbly.

Use a rectangle of paper about 20 x 8cm (8 x 3in), scissors and sticky tape.

1

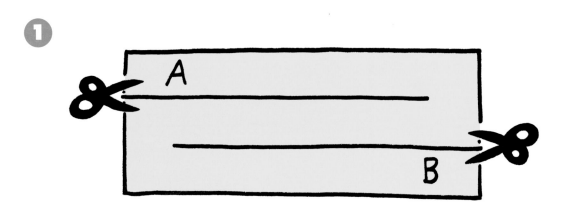

With scissors, very carefully cut line A, starting at the left, and line B, starting at the right. Try to divide the paper into three equal sections. To do the cutting well, you might want to measure the paper first and draw the lines before cutting them. Accuracy here will help the Helicopter to balance and spin well.

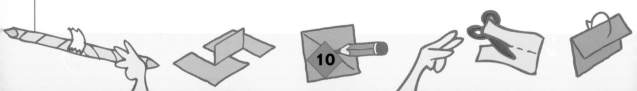

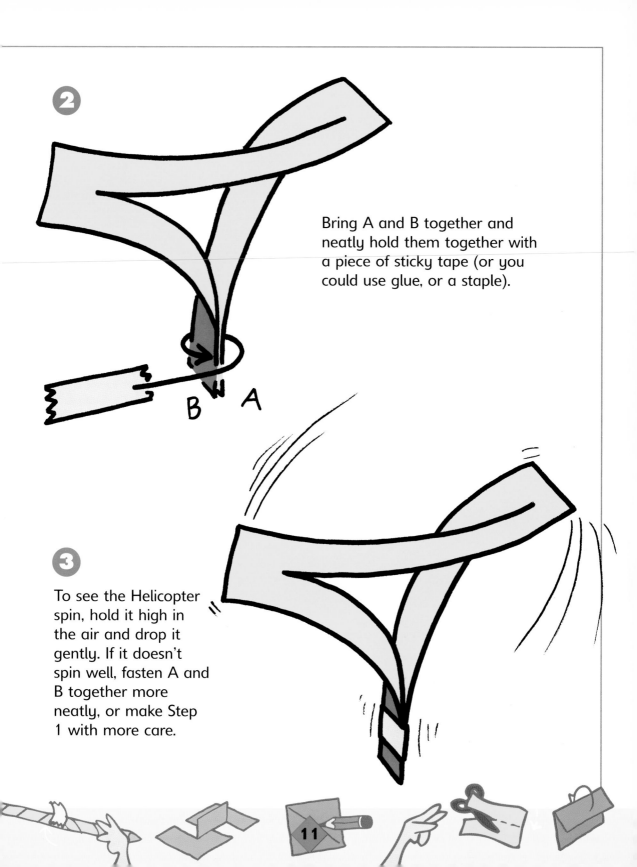

2

Bring A and B together and neatly hold them together with a piece of sticky tape (or you could use glue, or a staple).

B A

3

To see the Helicopter spin, hold it high in the air and drop it gently. If it doesn't spin well, fasten A and B together more neatly, or make Step 1 with more care.

Good Day, Bad Day?

I first learnt this trick many years ago, and it fascinates me as much now as it did then. Drawn carefully, the expression really does change a lot.

Use a sheet of ordinary paper and a felt-tip pen.

 1

On the paper, clearly draw a very simple face with big eyes and a thick straight line for the mouth. Try to make the mouth line begin and end exactly under the eyeballs.

Look at page 3 for the different folds.

2

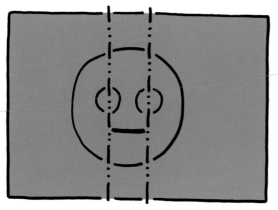

3

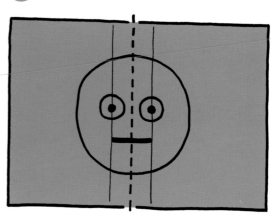

Very carefully make mountain creases which exactly touch the edges of the mouth, then go up through the middles of the eyes. This is very important if the illusion is to work well, so take your time to make the creases. Continue the creases to the top and bottom edges of the paper.

Finally, make a valley fold half way between the mountain folds.

4

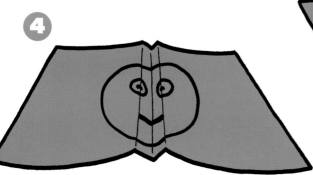

5

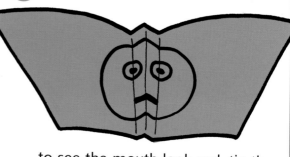

Pull open the creases. To make the mouth smile, tip the bottom edge of the paper towards you. This is a 'Good Day!' Then ...

... to see the mouth look sad, tip the top edge of the paper towards you. This is a 'Bad Day!' The trick will also work with heads on banknotes. Try it. You can also try tipping the paper to the left and right, so that the eyes appear to look left and right – the effect is very spooky!

Shapeshifter

This is similar to the 'Hide and Seek' trick on page 29, but instead of just showing new faces, it also changes its shape. It's also very, very addictive!

Use ordinary paper, pencil, ruler, glue and scissors.

1

Carefully measure a rectangle of paper to be 16 x 8cm (6 x 3in). Then, with a ruler and pencil, divide it into 2cm (³/₄in) squares. With scissors, cut off the corner squares. Also, cut out a rectangle to each side of the centre of the paper and make a slit connecting them.

Make a little snip in the middle, then cut carefully around the lines.

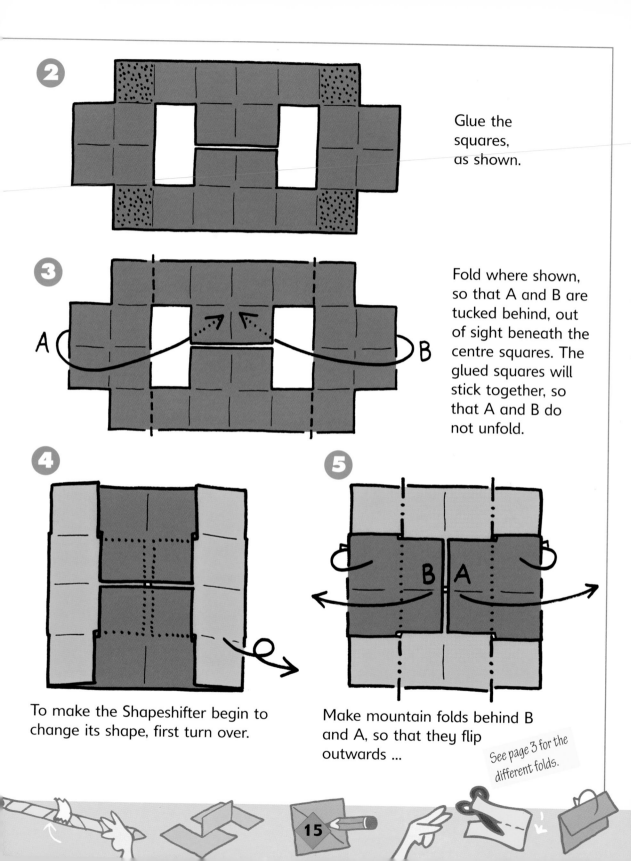

2 Glue the squares, as shown.

3 Fold where shown, so that A and B are tucked behind, out of sight beneath the centre squares. The glued squares will stick together, so that A and B do not unfold.

A

B

4 To make the Shapeshifter begin to change its shape, first turn over.

5 Make mountain folds behind B and A, so that they flip outwards ...

B A

See page 3 for the different folds.

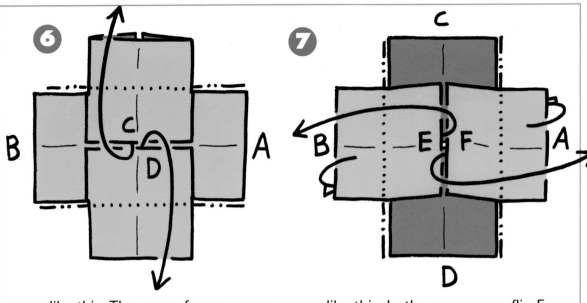

6 ... like this. The paper forms a cross shape. Now, make mountain folds behind C and D, so that they flip upwards and downwards ...

7 ... like this. In the same way, flip E and F outwards ...

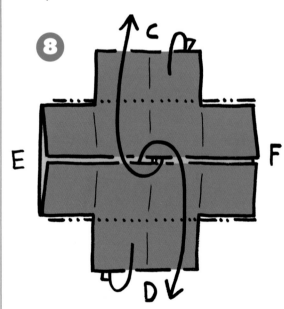

8 ... then flip C and D behind ...

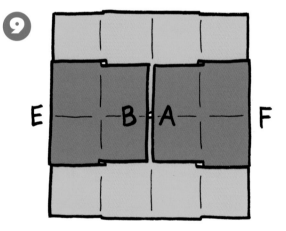

9 ... to return to Step 5!! Fold Steps 5 - 9 again, then fold them again, and again and again! For added effect, you can make each shape a different colour, or draw patterns that change as you fold, or write a secret message or perhaps invent a cartoon story.

Banger!

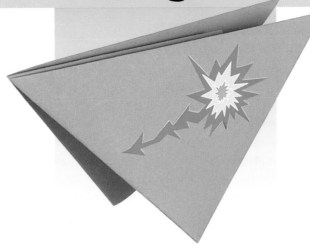

Use a large rectangle of paper.

This wonderful old design makes a loud "BANG!" when fired! For the noisiest results, use a big sheet of paper (but not a newspaper – the paper is too soft to make a noise).

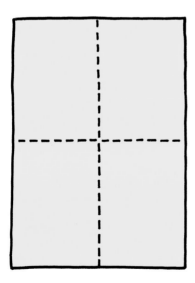

Fold in half across the middle in both directions, then unfold.

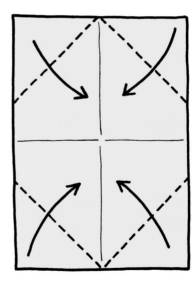

Fold the four corners to the centre crease.

3

Fold in half,
longways.

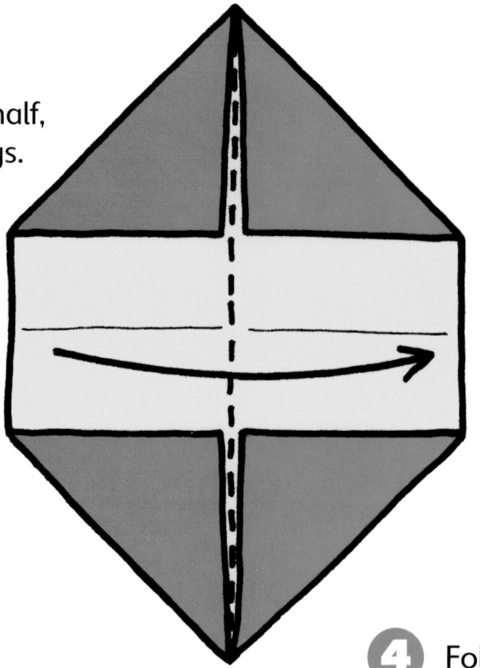

4 Fold A and B
across to the
right, creating
two big
triangles.

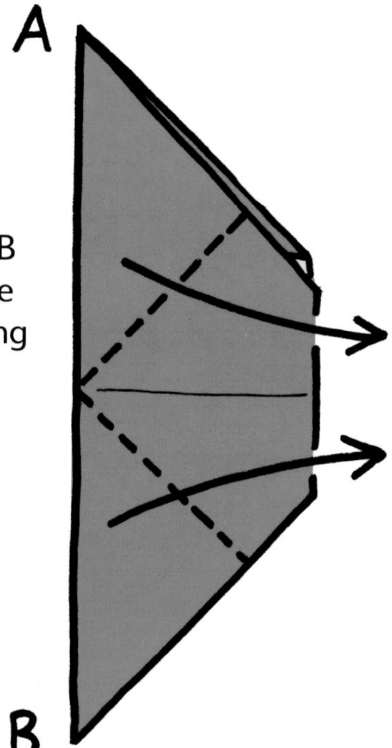

A

B

A B
B

5

Fold the top triangle
behind, so that A lies
behind B.

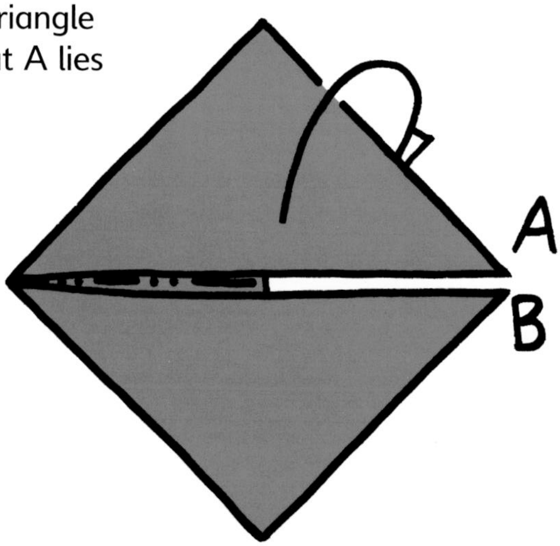

6 Your Banger is complete.

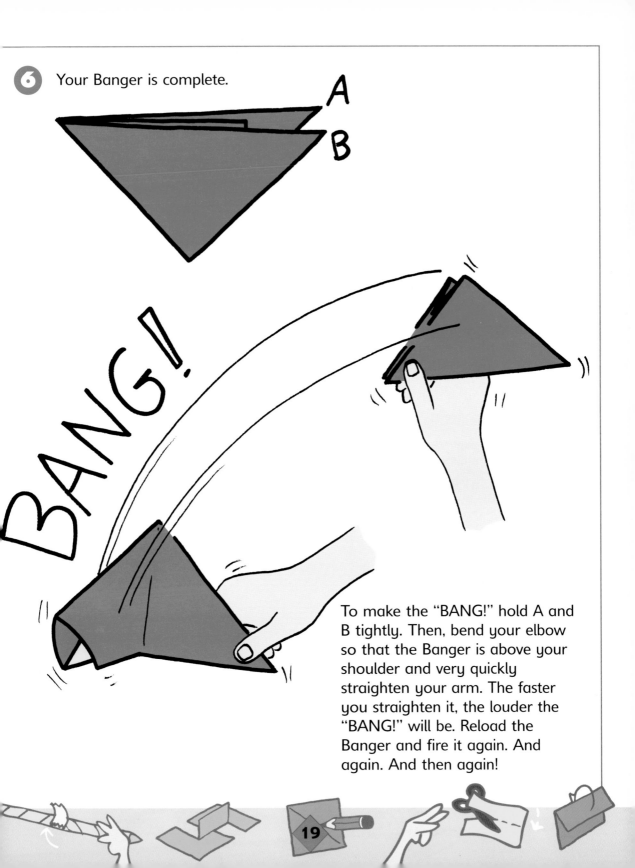

BANG!

To make the "BANG!" hold A and B tightly. Then, bend your elbow so that the Banger is above your shoulder and very quickly straighten your arm. The faster you straighten it, the louder the "BANG!" will be. Reload the Banger and fire it again. And again. And then again!

Downside Up

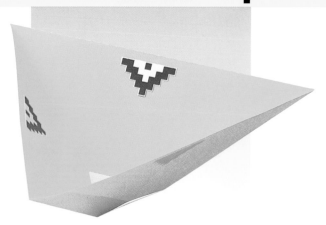

Use a sheet of ordinary paper, glue and scissors.

Challenge your friends to make a design which, when tossed into the air, will always land the same way up, but it is only one layer thick. The answer is very simple, but fun to make and to play with.

1

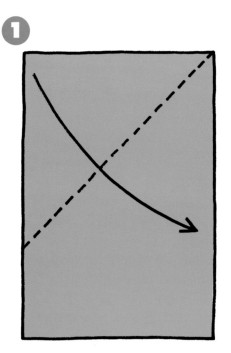

Fold a triangle.

2

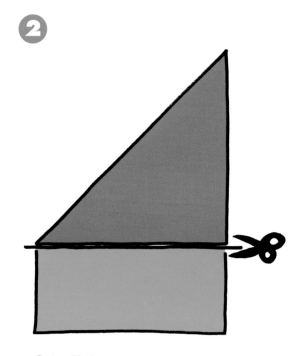

Cut off the extra paper.

3

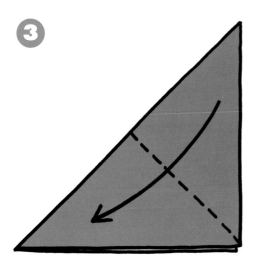

Fold the triangle in half.

4

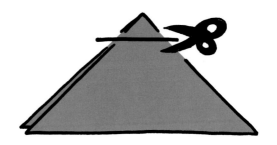

With scissors, cut off a small triangle at the top corner.

5

Unfold all the creases to make a flat square.

6

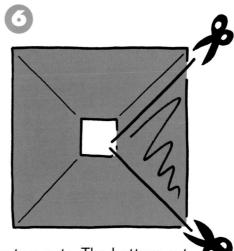

Make two cuts. The bottom cut follows the crease, but the top cut is a little below the crease just above it. Look carefully at the next drawing so that you are sure what to do.

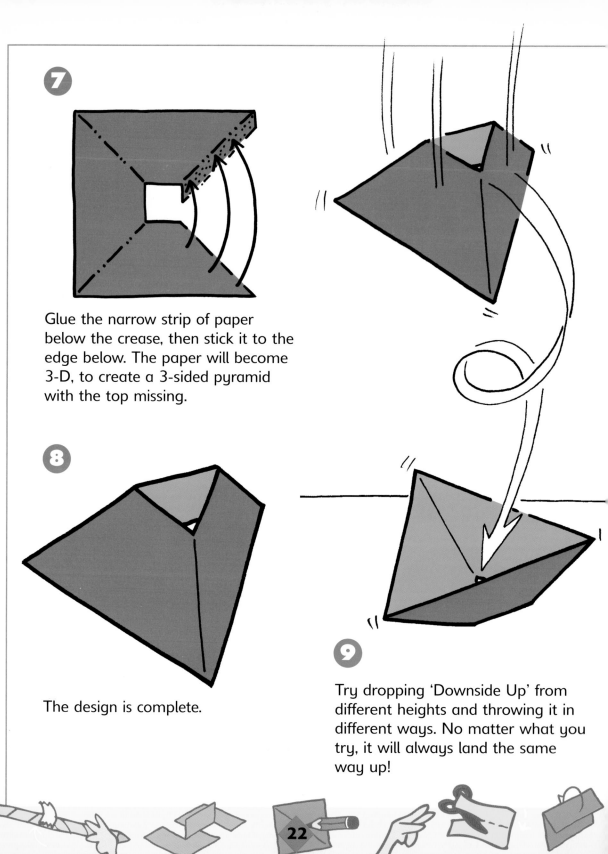

7

Glue the narrow strip of paper below the crease, then stick it to the edge below. The paper will become 3-D, to create a 3-sided pyramid with the top missing.

8

The design is complete.

9

Try dropping 'Downside Up' from different heights and throwing it in different ways. No matter what you try, it will always land the same way up!

S-t-r-e-t-c-h

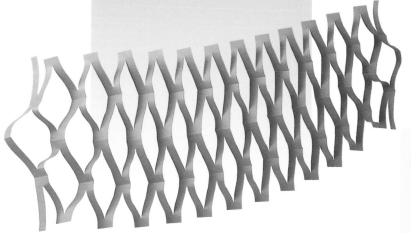

Use a sheet of ordinary paper and scissors.

You might know other ways to stretch paper by cutting, but this way is by far the best and also the most beautiful. However, it needs to be made very carefully, so take your time.

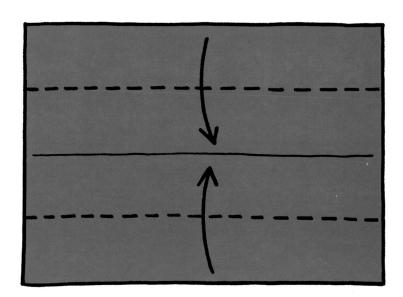

Crease and unfold across the middle, then fold the top and bottom edges to the centre crease.

See page 3 for the different folds.

2

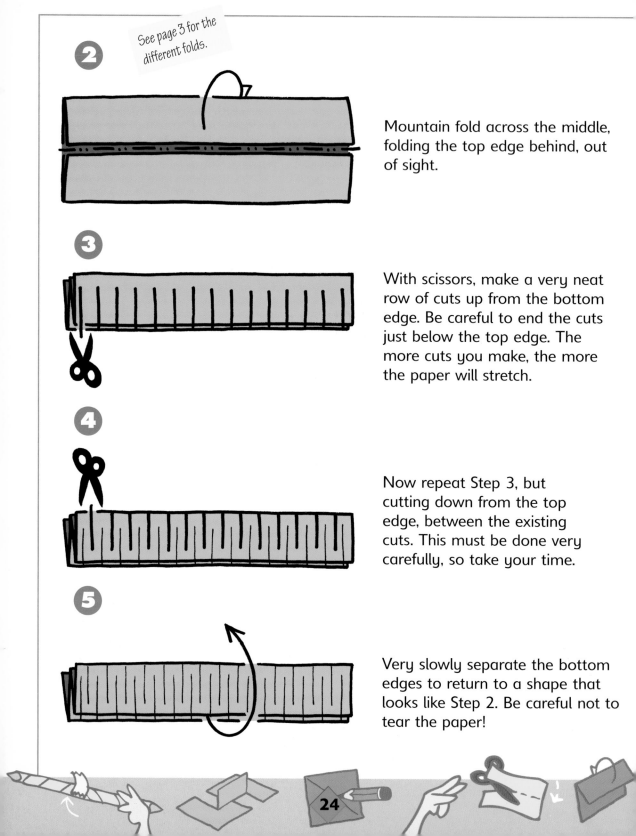

Mountain fold across the middle, folding the top edge behind, out of sight.

3

With scissors, make a very neat row of cuts up from the bottom edge. Be careful to end the cuts just below the top edge. The more cuts you make, the more the paper will stretch.

4

Now repeat Step 3, but cutting down from the top edge, between the existing cuts. This must be done very carefully, so take your time.

5

Very slowly separate the bottom edges to return to a shape that looks like Step 2. Be careful not to tear the paper!

24

6

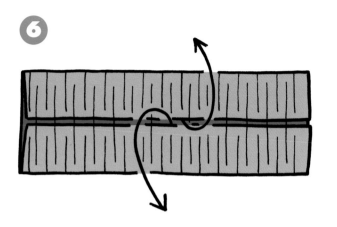

Now unfold the top and bottom creases to return to Step 1. All the creases have been unfolded – just the cuts remain.

7

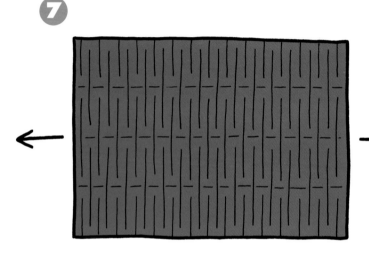

To s-t-r-e-t-c-h the paper, hold the edges and pull ...

8

... like this! Made from coloured paper or magazine pages, this amazing effect can be used to make beautiful decorations.

Exploding Underpants

Use a sheet of ordinary paper, scissors, glue and pencil.

Not many paper tricks start by looking as funny as this one ... and then do something so completely unbelievable when cut in half!

1

With scissors, cut out an upside-down letter T. You don't need to be too neat, but it helps to do it carefully.

2

With a pencil, neatly draw a line down the centre of the paper, but not right to the top. Repeat behind, too.

3

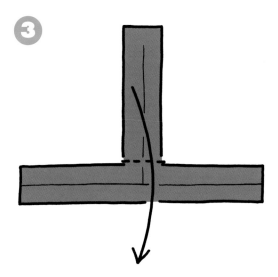

Fold down as shown, to make the T the right way up.

4

Bend the arms of the T into a circle and glue the ends very firmly together.

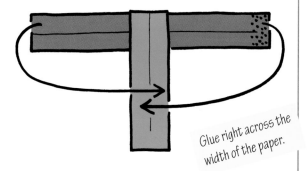

Glue right across the width of the paper.

5

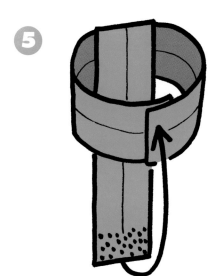

Finally, glue the loose end of the T firmly to the front of the circle.

6

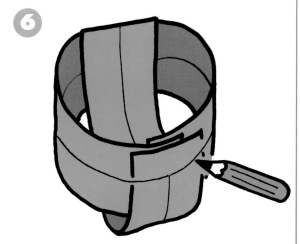

Join up the pencil lines at the front.

7

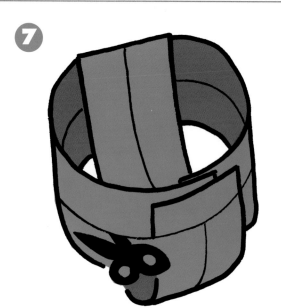

To explode the Underpants, use scissors to cut along the centre lines. Be very careful at the front and back to cut very neat, square forks where the lines divide, so that ...

8

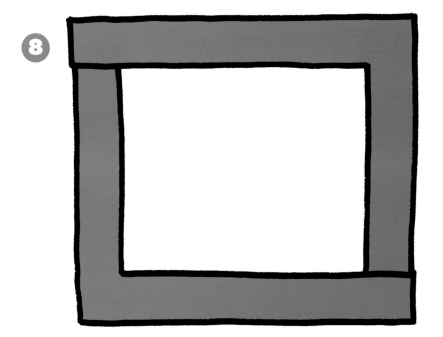

... you make the Underpants explode to create this amazing frame!!

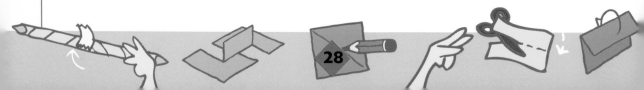

Hide and Seek

'Hide and Seek' is a very clever way to show pictures and messages, then mysteriously hide them inside the layers of the paper.

Use a sheet of ordinary paper, scissors and sticky tape.

1

Fold a rectangle of paper in half both ways, then fold the short quarter creases. Write numbers on the front, as shown, then turn over and write more numbers on the back. Make sure that 2 is on the back of 1, and so on.

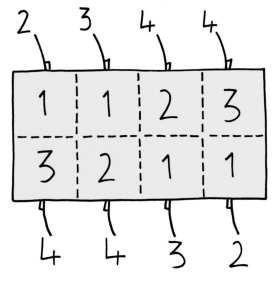

2

With scissors, make a cut as shown.

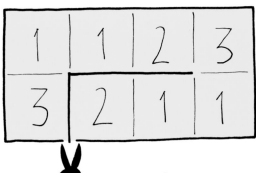

3

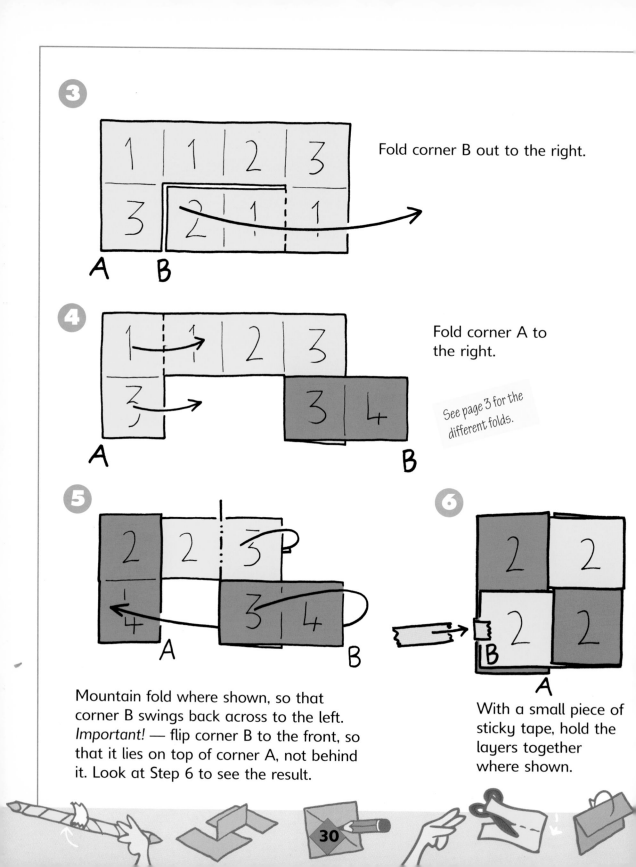

Fold corner B out to the right.

4

Fold corner A to the right.

See page 3 for the different folds.

5

Mountain fold where shown, so that corner B swings back across to the left. *Important!* — flip corner B to the front, so that it lies on top of corner A, not behind it. Look at Step 6 to see the result.

6

With a small piece of sticky tape, hold the layers together where shown.

7

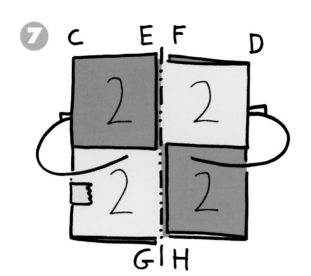

Sides 2 and 3 can be seen (side 3 is on the back). To find side 1, mountain fold down the middle …

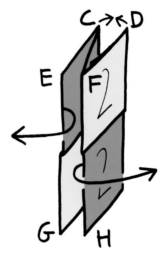

8

… then open the crease as though opening a book, separating F from E, and H from G. This is a very odd thing to do and seems wrong, but it isn't. When the paper is flat again, you will see …

9

… side 1!! To return to Step 7, turn over to side 2 and repeat Steps 7-9. Can you find side 4? (Hint: begin at side 3). With a little practice, you can easily move from side 1 to 2 to 3 to 4 and back again. To make 'Hide and Seek' more interesting, try colouring the sides, or cutting up magazine photos and gluing them on, or drawing pictures or cartoons, or writing messages or stories. You could even make one and give it to a friend as a birthday or Valentine's card with a special secret message.

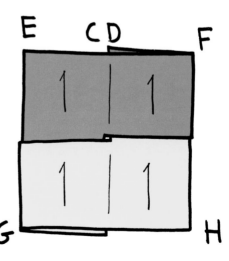

First published in Great Britain in 1999 by
MARY FORD BOOKS
a division of Michael O'Mara Holdings,
9 Lion Yard, Tremadoc Road, London SW4 7NQ

Amazing Paper Tricks that Really Work © 1999 Paul Jackson

Design: Chris Leishman Design
Photography: Meg Sullivan Photography

ISBN 1-85479-388-8

Printed in Hong Kong by Midas Printing Ltd.